Fantastic everyday Phonics practice from CGP!

CGP's Daily Practice Books are brilliant for building Phonics skills all the way through Year 1 — there's a mixed practice exercise for every day of the year.

What's more, they follow the National Curriculum 'Letters and Sounds' programme, so you can be sure they cover everything children need to learn.

This book is for the **Summer Term** of **Year 1**.

It covers the final part of **Phase 5** of the 'Letters and Sounds' programme, including:

- Alternative ways of spelling sounds

- The new sound "**zh**"

- More **tricky words** and **silent letters**

What CGP is all about

Our sole aim here at CGP is to produce the highest quality books — carefully written, immaculately presented and dangerously close to being funny.

Then we work our socks off to get them out to you — at the cheapest possible prices.

Contents

☑ Use the tick boxes to help keep a record of which tests have been attempted.

Week 9

Week 11

Week 10

Week 12

Published by CGP

ISBN: 978 1 78908 483 2

Written by Juliette Green

Editors: Daniel Fielding, Rebecca Greaves, Christopher Lindle, Sam Norman
Reviewer: Clare Leck

With thanks to Rosa Roberts and Lucy Towle for the proofreading.

Images throughout the book from www.edu-clips.com.

Printed by Elanders Ltd, Newcastle upon Tyne.
Based on the classic CGP style created by Richard Parsons.

How to Use this Book

This book is for children to complete in the Year 1 Summer Term. Each page looks like this:

The book is split into 12 weeks, with 5 days per week.

The box at the top of the page contains instructions. Read through these with your child and go through the worked example so they know what they're meant to do.

You will need to read through the instructions for any extension activities.

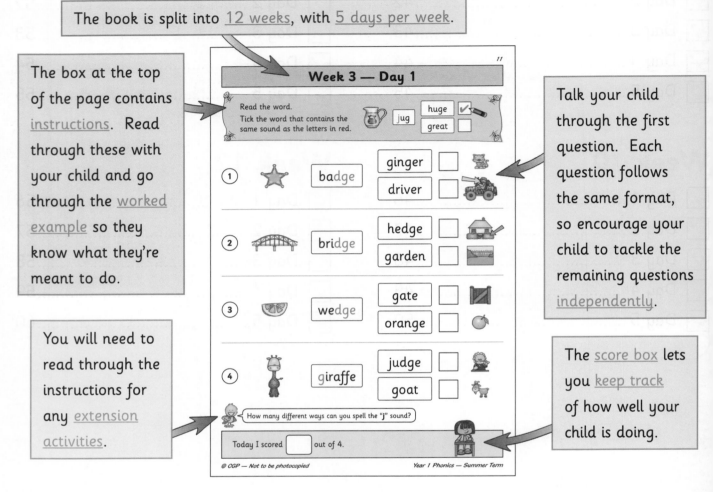

Talk your child through the first question. Each question follows the same format, so encourage your child to tackle the remaining questions independently.

The score box lets you keep track of how well your child is doing.

This book requires your child to match pictures to words.
You may need to help your child identify some pictures they're not sure of.

Phonics Hints for Helpers

Familiarise yourself with the features of this book below before you begin:

- Word frames are used in spelling and writing activities. There is one box for each sound. A sound can consist of more than one letter.

- Tricky words are words with letters that have a sound that does not correspond to the expected sound, or that have a sound that has not yet been learned. Tricky words are written into blue boxes.

Week 1 — Day 1

Read each word.
Tick the word that contains the same sound as the letters in red.

fish — dolphin ✓ / shrimp ☐

1. ele**ph**ant — frog ☐ / tiger ☐

2. **f**airy — dragon ☐ / **ph**antom ☐

3. tro**ph**y — sofa ☐ / chair ☐

4. tra**ff**ic — **ph**onics ☐ / maths ☐

How many different ways can you spell the "**f**" sound?

Today I scored ☐ out of 4.

Week 1 — Day 2

① what wat

② whell well

③  wale whale

④ web wheb

⑤  wheel weel

⑥ when wen

⑦  wiskers whiskers

Today I scored ☐ out of 7.

Week 1 — Day 3

Read the caption.
Underline all the letters that make the "**i**" sound.

the b<u>i</u>ggest crystal

1 pyramids in Egypt

2 grinning gymnasts

3 the adding symbol

4 Glyn and his igloo

5 drink milk in the gym

6 a mystery gift for Lynn who is fifty

Today I scored ☐ out of 21.

Year 1 Phonics — Summer Term

Week 1 — Day 4

Read this short story. Underline all the words that have an "**e**" sound. Three words have been underlined for you. There are 18 more to find.

Sleepy <u>Stefan</u>

<u>Stefan</u> had <u>read</u> a creepy story at bedtime. This meant he had not slept well. He woke up feeling dreadful.

He went downstairs and his mum had made him a very pleasant breakfast. He had three eggs and red jam spread onto some bread.

Stefan felt so much better. He was ready to go outside and play in the sunny weather.

What are the different ways of spelling the "**e**" sound?

Today I scored [ ] out of 18.

Week 1 — Day 5

Read each sentence. Draw a line to match it to the best picture.

Mrs Tran likes to play golf.

1 The little girl used the letters of the alphabet.

2 Phil drew a graph in maths.

3 Frankie looked at the headlines.

4 Mr Phipps asked her to smile for the photo.

5 The bird family puffed out their feathers.

How many tricky words can you spot in these sentences?

Today I scored ☐ out of 5.

Year 1 Phonics — Summer Term

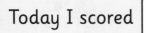

Week 2 — Day 1

Read the word.
Tick the word that contains the same sound as the letters in red. down | behind ☐ | around ✓

1  **hound** — cowshed ☐ | pigsty ☐

2  **towel** — toilet ☐ | spout ☐

3  **shouting** — howling ☐ | snarling ☐

4  **cloudy** — showery ☐ | stormy ☐

 How many different ways can you spell the "**ow**" sound?

Today I scored 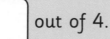 out of 4.

Week 2 — Day 2

Look at the picture. Then circle the correct word.

(wander) wonder

1
| wond | wand |

2
| washing | woshing |

3
| swon | swan |

4
| squatting | squotting |

5
| wosp | wasp |

6
| wollet | wallet |

 What happens to the sound of the letter '**a**' in these words?

Today I scored [ ] out of 6.

Year 1 Phonics — Summer Term

Week 2 — Day 3

Read the word.
Underline the silent
letter in the word.

 bom<u>b</u>s

---

(1) lamb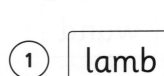

(2) thumb

(3) climb

(4) comb

(5) crumb

(6) plumber

(7) salmon

(8) yolk

 Say the letters you have underlined in these words.

Today I scored [ ] out of 8.

Week 2 — Day 4

Read the sentence.
Underline all the words that have an "**oi**" sound.

The <u>boy</u> is <u>pointing</u>.

1 The children enjoy playing with noisy toys.

2 They found coins and oysters at the bottom of the sea.

3 The cowboy coils his rope but the bull avoids it.

4 On a boiling hot day, the wasps were annoying me.

5 The school employs him to grow plants in the soil.

 What are the different ways of spelling the "**oi**" sound?

Today I scored [ ] out of 12.

Year 1 Phonics — Summer Term

Week 2 — Day 5

Read the question.
Colour the correct answer.

Where is the lamb?

in a field

in a cloud

1 Could a plant grow if it was dead?

yes

no

2 Who are these people?

clowns

royals

3 Do owls have thumbs?

yes

no

4 What is the prince climbing?

a tower

a tree

5 Would a frog live in a swamp?

yes

no

How many tricky words can you spot in these questions?

Today I scored ☐ out of 5.

Week 3 — Day 1

 Read the word.
Tick the word that contains the same sound as the letters in red.

 jug huge ✔
great

1 **badge** ginger
driver

2  **bridge** hedge
garden

3 **wedge** gate
orange

4  **giraffe** judge
goat

 How many different ways can you spell the "**j**" sound?

Today I scored [ ] out of 4.

Year 1 Phonics — Summer Term

Week 3 — Day 2

Read the word.
Underline the silent letter in the word.

<u>g</u>narl  <u>k</u>nead

1 gnome

5 knot

2 knit

6 design

3 sign

7 knight

4 kneel

8 knock

Say the letters you have underlined in these words.

Today I scored ☐ out of 8.

Week 3 — Day 3

Read the sentence.
Underline all the words that have a "**ch**" sound.

He had a <u>beach</u> <u>adventure</u>.

1 Did you stitch a patch on my jeans?

2 The chick is hatching from an egg.

3 I took a picture of our kitchen.

4 This creature is scratching an itch.

5 The witch was stirring her mixture.

What are the different ways of spelling the "**ch**" sound?

Today I scored [ ] out of 11.

Year 1 Phonics — Summer Term

Week 3 — Day 4

Read this letter. Underline all the words that have an "**ear**" sound. Three words have been underlined for you. There are 12 more to find.

Dear Mum,

I am having a great time <u>here</u> at camp. Today I saw a <u>deer</u> appear right near my tent! I sat inside, peering at it. I did not interfere with it.

Yesterday I got severe fear when I was climbing. I nearly shed a tear. As I got to the top I could clearly hear my mates cheering!

See you soon,
Meera xx

What are the different ways of spelling the "**ear**" sound?

Today I scored ☐ out of 12.

Week 3 — Day 5

Read each sentence. Draw a line to match it to the best picture.

Oh, was that a badger?

1 We like to go outside to enjoy nature.

2 This shape is called a sphere.

3 Mum could not steer. We had a puncture.

4 My dad grew a beard so he could be Santa.

5 Mr Beeching works as a butcher.

 How many tricky words can you spot in these sentences?

Today I scored ☐ out of 5.

Year 1 Phonics — Summer Term

Week 4 — Day 1

Read the word.
Tick the word that contains the same sound as the letters in red.

snow

neck ☐
face ✔

1. house — city ☐ — cottage ☐

2. December — sheep ☐ — geese ☐

3. scientist — planet ☐ — muscle ☐

4. pencil — scissors ☐ — ruler ☐

How many different ways can you spell the "**s**" sound?

Today I scored ☐ out of 4.

Week 4 — Day 2

Read the word.
Underline the silent
letter in the word.

listening

1. whistle

2. nestle

3. glisten

4. rustle

5. bristles

6. castle

7. fasten

8. mistletoe

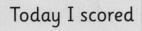 Say the letter you have underlined in these words.

Today I scored ☐ out of 8.

Year 1 Phonics — Summer Term

Week 4 — Day 3

Read the sentence.
Underline all the words that have the "**air**" sound.

The <u>bear</u> sat on the spare <u>chair</u>.

(1) To be fair, we will share this pear.

(2) Where is the mare? In the square field.

(3) How dare you stare at my new haircut!

(4) Don't scare the hares. They are everywhere.

(5) If you don't wear clothes, you are bare.

What are the different ways of spelling the "**air**" sound?

Today I scored [ ] out of 14.

Week 4 — Day 4

Copy one of the words to complete the sentence.

| Mrs | Dee is my step-mum. |

Practise writing the words first.

| oh | Mr | Mrs | called |

1 [ ] look, there is a mouse.

2 [ ] Harris has a pet goose.

3 [ ] Burton is floating down.

4 A nice smell is

[ ] a scent.

5 A female horse is

[ ] a mare.

Check your work. Did you use capital letters at the start of the sentences?

Today I scored [ ] out of 5.

Year 1 Phonics — Summer Term

Week 4 — Day 5

Read each sentence. Draw a line to match it to the best picture.

Where should we go next?

 1 Kris thought he would iron the creases out.

2 Look through the window at the scene.

3 Holly is playing with her food again.

4 James chooses words for his sentence.

5 Many wild animals are scared of people.

How many tricky words can you spot in these sentences?

Today I scored ☐ out of 5.

Week 5 — Day 1

Read the caption.
Then colour the picture that matches.

flight

1 flies

2 night sky

3 tied up

4 shiny prize

5 a spider writing

6 kind, polite child

7 high pylon

How many different ways can you spell the "**igh**" sound?

Today I scored [ ] out of 7.

Week 5 — Day 2

Look at the picture.
Circle the correct
word for the picture.

rise	rose

1

toes	ties

2

ripe	rope

3

spoke	spike

4

dize	doze

5

croed	cried

6

volcanoes	volcanies

Today I scored [ ] out of 6.

Week 5 — Day 3

Read these facts. Underline all the words that have an "**oa**" sound. Three words have been underlined for you. There are 14 more to find.

The <u>Romans</u>

* These people came from <u>Rome</u> in Italy. They ruled many parts of the <u>globe</u>.

* There were many Roman heroes. One hero was Jason who had a ship called the Argo.

* Slaves had to row the boats. It was dark under the deck with no windows.

* When the Romans first came to England it was too chilly so they went back home.

* The Romans made lots of roads.

* These people are wearing togas.

 What are the different ways of spelling the "**oa**" sound?

Today I scored [   ] out of 14.

Year 1 Phonics — Summer Term

Week 5 — Day 4

Write the sentence into the word frames.

| I am called Joe. | I | a m | called | J | oe | . |

(1) This exercise is called yoga.

(2) My pet goat is called Brian.

(3) This reptile is called a gecko.

Today I scored ⬚ out of 3.

Week 5 — Day 5

Read each sentence. Draw a line to match it to the best picture.

She laughed at my reply.

1 The unkind girls laughed behind her back.

2 The troll laughed at the little billy goat.

3 The hippo in a bow tie laughed and smiled.

4 The children laughed at the clown show.

5 They all laughed when Simon got slimed.

 Circle the word '**laughed**' in these sentences.

Today I scored ☐ out of 5.

Year 1 Phonics — Summer Term

Week 6 — Day 1

Read the word.
Tick the word that contains the same sound as the letters in red.

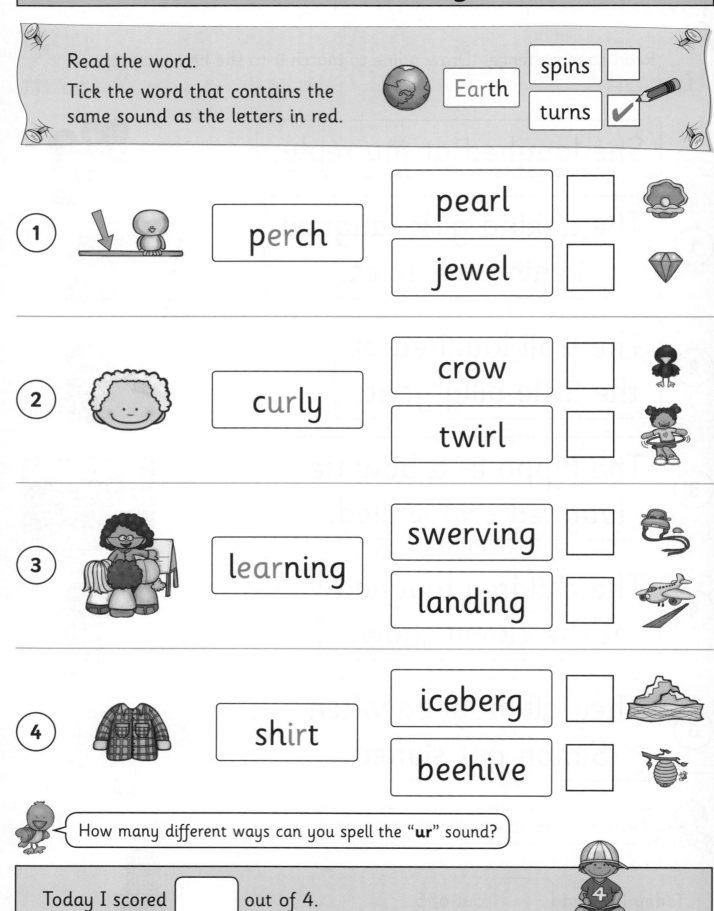

Earth | spins ☐ | turns ✓

1 | perch | pearl ☐ | jewel ☐

2 | curly | crow ☐ | twirl ☐

3 | learning | swerving ☐ | landing ☐

4 | shirt | iceberg ☐ | beehive ☐

How many different ways can you spell the "**ur**" sound?

Today I scored ☐ out of 4.

Week 6 — Day 2

Look at the picture.
Then circle the word
that is spelt correctly.

 | wurse | worse |

1    words   wurds

2   wurm   worm

3   wurkout   workout

4    worship   wurship

5    wurld   world

 What happens to the sound of the letters
'**or**' when they come after the letter '**w**'?

Today I scored ☐ out of 5.

     Year 1 Phonics — Summer Term

Week 6 — Day 3

Read the sentence.
Underline all the words that have the "**c**" sound.

Kit has
<u>black</u> <u>socks</u>.

1 Nick had a headache at his school desk.

2 Katie skips and flies her kite high in the sky.

3 Jackson found a lucky ticket in his jacket pocket.

£100

4 After working, Becky had a soak with her duck.

5 The cook baked pink cupcakes for the party.

 What are the different ways of spelling the "**c**" sound?

Today I scored [ ] out of 21.

Week 6 — Day 4

Write the sentence in the word frames.

Oh dear, he is hurt.

| Oh | d | ear | , | he | i | s | h | ur | t | . |

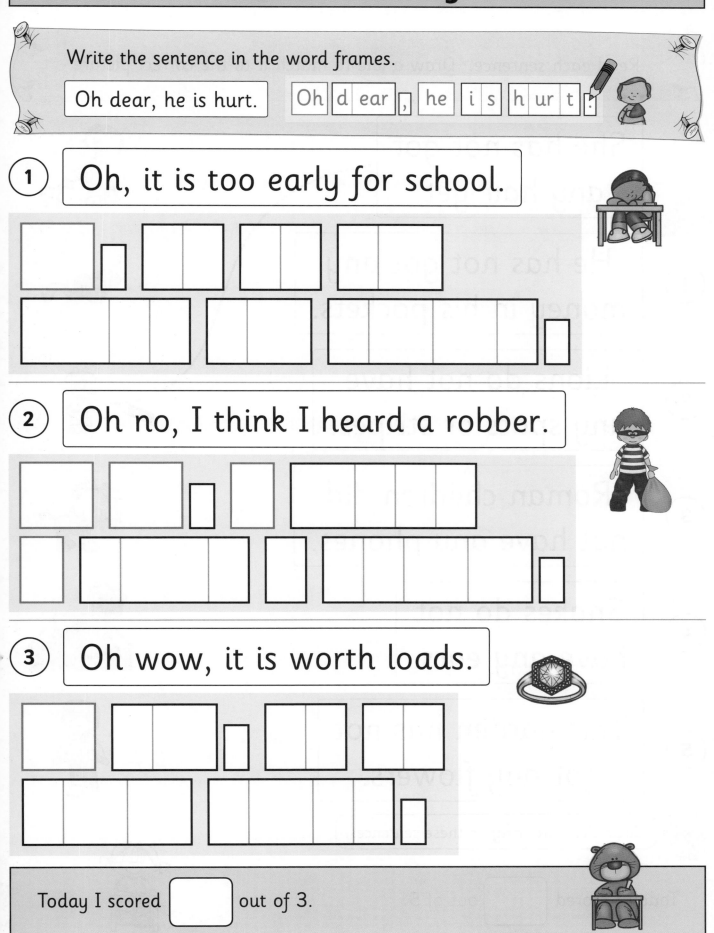

1 Oh, it is too early for school.

2 Oh no, I think I heard a robber.

3 Oh wow, it is worth loads.

Today I scored ☐ out of 3.

Week 6 — Day 5

Read each sentence. Draw a line to match it to the correct picture.

She has not got any hair yet.

1 He has not got any money in his pockets.

2 Lions do not have any spots or stripes.

3 Roman children did not have any phones.

4 Snakes do not have any ears.

5 This garden has not got any flowers.

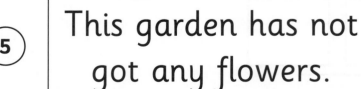

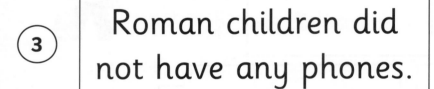

Circle the word '**any**' in these sentences.

Today I scored ☐ out of 5.

Week 7 — Day 1

Read the word.
Tick the word that contains the same sound as the letters in red.

jewel

suit ✔

coal ☐

1. clues

nail ☐

screws ☐

2. flute

poppy ☐

tissues ☐

3. toucan

hooting ☐

quacking ☐

4. fruit

pear ☐

prune ☐

How many different ways can you spell the **long** "**oo**" sound?

Today I scored ☐ out of 4.

Year 1 Phonics — Summer Term

Week 7 — Day 2

Read the caption.
Then colour the correct picture.

rescue

1 fumes from the tube

2 huge pot of stew

3 a cute mule

4 argue over the cube

5 use a computer

6 mute the bad tune

7 view the new statue

 How many different ways can you spell the "**yoo**" sound?

Today I scored ☐ out of 7.

Week 7 — Day 3

Read the sentence.
Underline all the words that have the short "**oo**" sound.

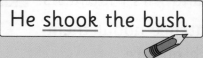

He <u>shook</u> the <u>bush</u>.

1 We could look for facts in this book.

2 You should not go into a field with a bull.

3 He was pulling my hair but it was not playful.

4 The crook took a plate of cookies and a pudding.

5 I would like a cushion to put behind my back.

 You may pronounce these words differently so don't worry if you can only find some of them.

Today I scored ☐ out of 14.

Year 1 Phonics — Summer Term

Week 7 — Day 4

This is Mr and Mrs Matthews.
Write a sentence about them
next to each picture.

 Remember to use capital letters and full stops.

1

2

3

Today I wrote [ ] sentences.

Week 7 — Day 5

Read each sentence. Draw a line to match it to the best picture.

Andrew was once rescued by a dog.

(1) Once upon a time, there were three bears.

(2) There was once a fairy who knew lots of magic.

(3) Should you only brush your teeth once a day?

(4) Jules once stood in glue wearing his new boots.

(5) My nephew Bruce once had a smart blue suit.

Circle the word '**once**' in these sentences.

Today I scored [ ] out of 5.

Year 1 Phonics — Summer Term

Week 8 — Day 1

Read the caption.
Underline all the
"**ee**" sounds.

 three times ten
equals thirty

 If the "**ee**" sound is made using a split digraph, use a loop like this: these

(1) green leaf on a tee shirt

(2) donkey, turkey and sheep

(3) a very happy priest

(4) athlete on a trapeze

(5) a sneaky cookie thief

(6) steaming pan of peas

(7) a beehive of sticky honey

Today I scored [ ] out of 20.

Week 8 — Day 2

Read this short story. Underline all the words that have an '**ee**' sound. Three words have been underlined for you. There are 30 more to find.

The <u>Secret</u> <u>Party</u>

<u>Pete</u> was feeling unhappy. Today was his birthday but people had forgotten. He went out to speak to the sheep in the field.

Suddenly, Pete heard a shriek. He saw his sister Eve leap out from behind a tree. Then Mummy, Daddy and his brother Steven jumped out too. His Auntie came out with a tray of sweet treats. There was wobbly jelly, runny ice cream and sticky lollies.

He got some money and his best gift was a funny toy monkey.

 What are the different ways of spelling the "**ee**" sound?

Today I scored [ ] out of 30.

Year 1 Phonics — Summer Term

Week 8 — Day 3

Read the word.
Underline the silent letter
at the start of the word.

 w<u>r</u>eck

1 wrap

2 wreath

3 wring

4 wrist

5 write

6 wren

7 wrapping

8 wrestling

 Say the letter you have underlined in these words.

Today I scored [ ] out of 8.

Week 8 — Day 4

Copy one of the words to complete the sentence.

The | people | rode donkeys.

their   looked

asked   people

Practise writing the words first.

1 The chief [   ]

us to tell her our names.

2 The Queen Bee [   ]

for a hole to make her nest.

3 [   ]   in Egypt made

[   ]   kings and queens

into mummies.

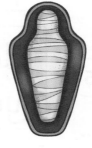

Today I scored [   ] out of 4.

Year 1 Phonics — Summer Term

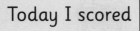

Week 8 — Day 5

Read each sentence. Draw a line to match it to the correct picture.

Can I have some dinner please?

① Please let it be sunny for our garden party.

② Puppies like to please their owners.

③ Please feed my donkey when I am on holiday.

④ You should always say please and thank you.

⑤ Please take turns when you are on the swing.

Thank you!

 Circle the word '**please**' in these sentences.

Today I scored ☐ out of 5.

Week 9 — Day 1

Read the word.
Tick the word that contains the same sound as the letters in red.

 rain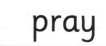

| great | ✓ |
| coat | |

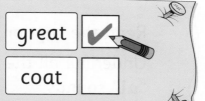

1 pr**ey**

| pray | |
| press | |

2  v**ei**l

| pinecone | |
| acorn | |

3  n**eigh**

| chain | |
| soap | |

4  sk**a**tes

| disobey | |
| pinch | |

 How many different ways can you spell the "**ai**" sound?

Today I scored ☐ out of 4.

 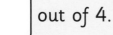

Week 9 — Day 2

Read the caption.
Underline all the "**ai**" sounds.

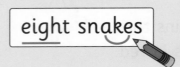

eight sn<u>a</u>kes

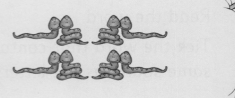

If the "**ai**" sound is made using a split digraph, use a loop like this: ace

1 a grey crayon

2 escape the maze

3 baby potatoes

4 bales of hay

5 make it with clay

6 reindeer and sleigh

7 face painting is great

Today I scored ☐ out of 15.

Year 1 Phonics — Summer Term © CGP — Not to be photocopied

Week 9 — Day 3

Look at the picture.
Then circle the word
that is spelt correctly.

| leavs | (leaves) |

1. move | mov

2. abov | above

3. love | lov

4. glovs | gloves

5. serve | serv

6. massive | massiv

7. detectiv | detective

Today I scored [ ] out of 7.

Year 1 Phonics — Summer Term

Week 9 — Day 4

Write the sentence in the word frames.

He asked for help.

| He | asked | f o r | h e l p . |

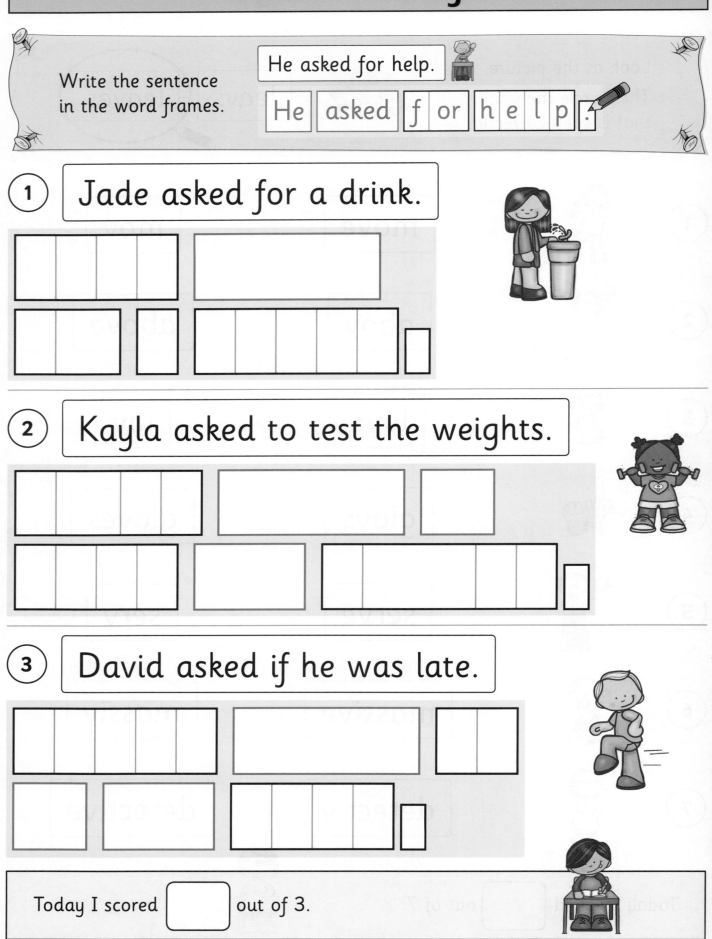

1 Jade asked for a drink.

2 Kayla asked to test the weights.

3 David asked if he was late.

Today I scored ☐ out of 3.

Week 9 — Day 5

Read the sentence.
Then draw a picture to match.

I have three best friends.

1 My friends and I like to play games.

2 I gave my friend a birthday cake.

Today I scored ☐ out of 2.

Year 1 Phonics — Summer Term

Week 10 — Day 1

Read the word.
Tick the word that contains the same sound as the letters in red.

lawn | catch ☐ | walk ✔

1. snore — fourteen ☐ 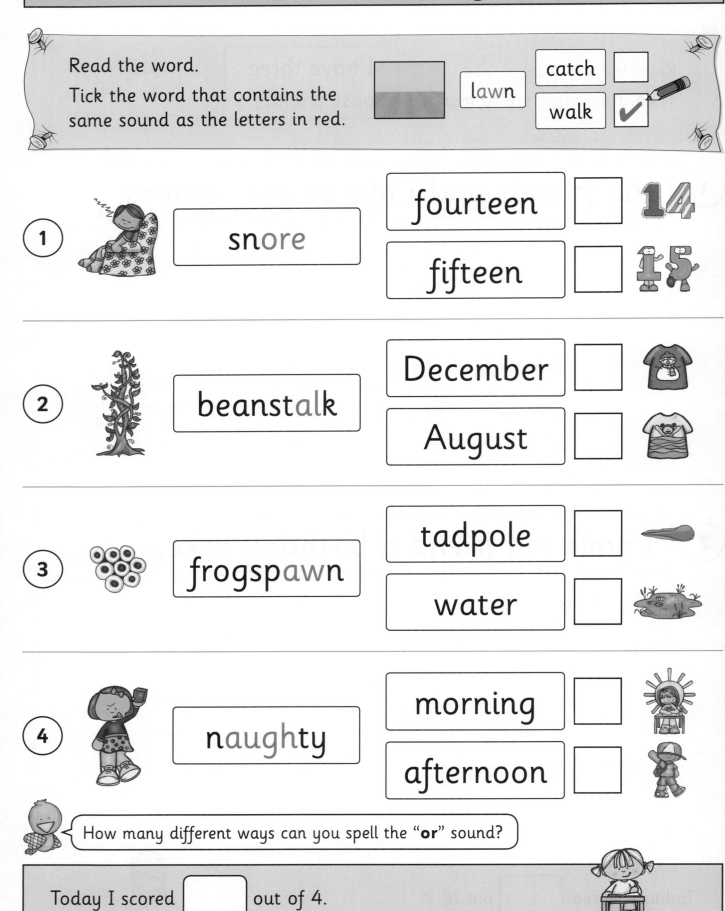 | fifteen ☐

2. beanstalk — December ☐ | August ☐

3. frogspawn — tadpole ☐ | water ☐

4. naughty — morning ☐ | afternoon ☐

How many different ways can you spell the "**or**" sound?

Today I scored ☐ out of 4.

Week 10 — Day 2

Read the word.

Then write a rhyming word in the word frame.

The picture will help.

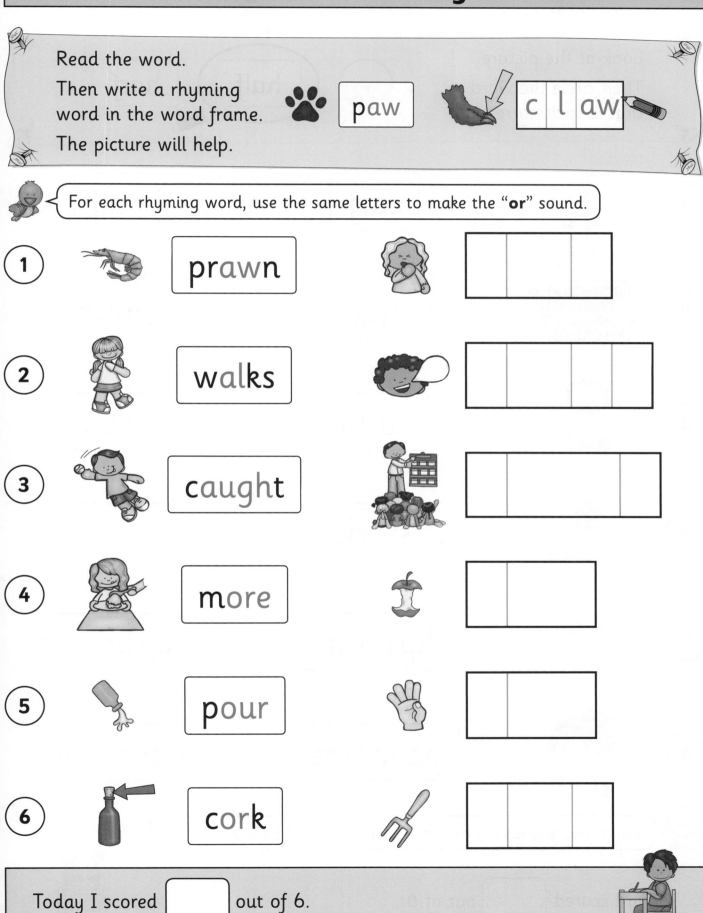

paw

c l aw

For each rhyming word, use the same letters to make the "**or**" sound.

1. prawn

2. walks

3. caught

4. more

5. pour

6. cork

Today I scored ☐ out of 6.

Week 10 — Day 3

Look at the picture.
Then circle the word
that is spelt correctly.

| half | harf |

1 | carf | calf |

2 | chalk | chork |

3 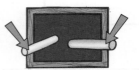 | carm | calm |

4 | stork | stalk |

5 | lip barm | lip balm |

6 | palm tree | parm tree |

 Which two sounds did the letters '**al**' make in the correct words?

Today I scored [ ] out of 6.

Week 10 — Day 4

Write the sentence in the word frames.

Seth looked awful.

| S | e | t | h | | l | o | o | k | e | d | | a | w | | f | u | l | | . |

1 Dawn looked at herself.

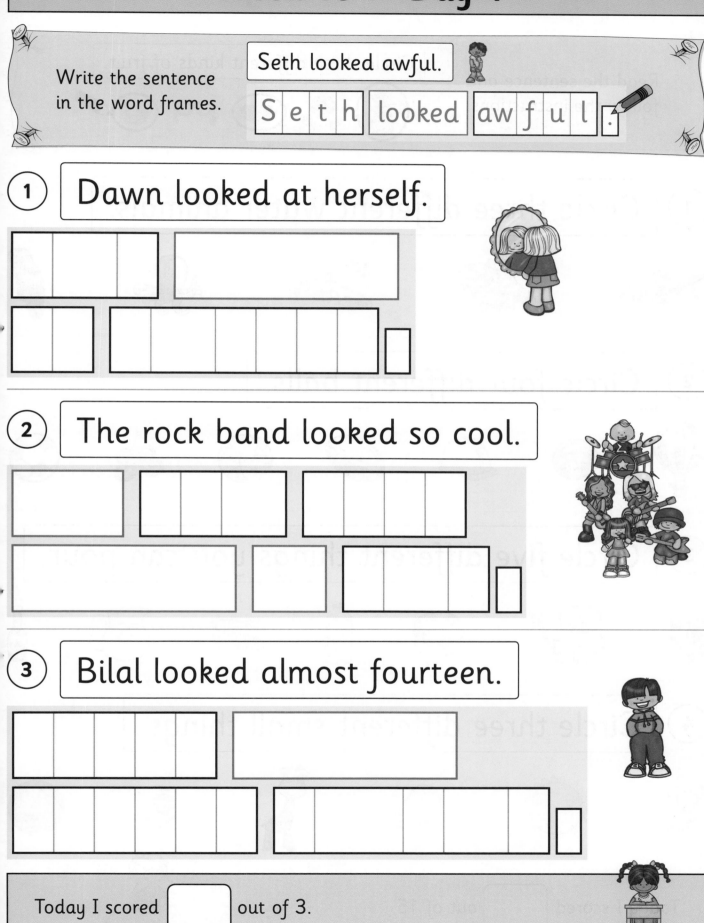

2 The rock band looked so cool.

3 Bilal looked almost fourteen.

Today I scored ☐ out of 3.

Year 1 Phonics — Summer Term

Week 10 — Day 5

Read the sentence and follow the instructions.

Circle three different kinds of fruit.

(1) Circle three different water animals.

(2) Circle four different balls.

(3) Circle five different things you can pour.

(4) Circle three different small things.

Today I scored [ ] out of 15.

Week 11 — Day 1

Look at the picture.
Then circle the word or caption that is spelt correctly.

 pauze | (pause)

1.  pleaze | please

2. noise | noize

3. bruized | bruised

4. take it eazy | take it easy

5. cruize ship | cruise ship

6. leg raises | leg raizes

 Can you see how the letter 's' sometimes makes a "z" sound?

Today I scored [ ] out of 6.

Year 1 Phonics — Summer Term

Week 11 — Day 2

Read the sentence.
Underline all the words that have the "**sh**" sound.

The <u>patient</u> had too much <u>sugar</u>.

1. Shane was the official chef at the mansion.

2. Michelle went for a special facial and pampering session.
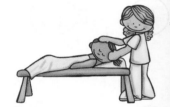

3. Kash went on a mission to the space station.

4. The musician was sure she would be a star.

5. Charlene and Sheena had a discussion about fashion.

What are the different ways of spelling the "**sh**" sound?

Today I scored ☐ out of 18.

Week 11 — Day 3

Read the word.
Colour the best picture to match the word.

 pleasure

1 treasure

2 vision

3 measuring

4 television

5 casual

6 collision

 Can you hear the new "**zh**" sound in all these words?

Today I scored ☐ out of 6.

Year 1 Phonics — Summer Term

Week 11 — Day 4

Write the sentence in the word frames.

They gave their score.

| They | g a v e | their | s c ore | . |

1 The dancers took their places.

2 The children read their book.

3 They ate their posh dinner.

Today I scored [ ] out of 3.

Week 11 — Day 5

Read each sentence. Draw a line to match it to the best picture.

We use our
eyes for vision.

1 Did you know that
spiders have eight eyes?

2 The mouse had its
eyes on the cheese.

3 There were three pairs of
creepy eyes in the dark.

4 All eyes were fixed
on the red carpet.

5 She kept her eyes
on the teacher.

Circle the word '**eyes**' in these sentences.

Today I scored ☐ out of 5.

Year 1 Phonics — Summer Term

Week 12 — Day 1

Read the sentence.

Underline all the words that **end** with the short "**er**" sound.

The <u>doctor</u> made me lie on <u>a</u> sofa.

(1) The famous actor said he never felt nervous.

(2) The circus ringmaster was not afraid of the lion.

(3) The visitor was a clever author.

(4) The lemon colour drink was really melon flavour.

Can you find any words that have the short "**er**" sound in the **middle** of the word?

(5) The camel ate a cactus in the desert.

Today I scored ☐ out of 17.

Week 12 — Day 2

Read the word and circle the correct picture.

puddle		

 1 | cuddle | | |

 2 | squabble |  | |

 3 | prickle | |  |

 4 | wobble | | |

 5 | single | |  |

 6 | dangle | | |

Can you name the rest of the pictures that you did not circle? All the words end with the letters '**le**'.

Today I scored ☐ out of 6.

Year 1 Phonics — Summer Term

58

Week 12 — Day 3

Read the word. Then draw a line to match it to the rhyming word.

  Remember rhyming words can have different spelling patterns.

	pray	birds
(1)	lime	honey
(2)	pier	grey
(3)	scares	climb
(4)	sunny	stairs
(5)	bubble	hawk
(6)	stork	double
(7)	words	steer

Today I scored [ ] out of 7.

Year 1 Phonics — Summer Term   © CGP — Not to be photocopied

Week 12 — Day 4

Write a sentence next to each picture.
Use the word '**people**' in each sentence.

Remember to use capital letters and full stops.

(1)

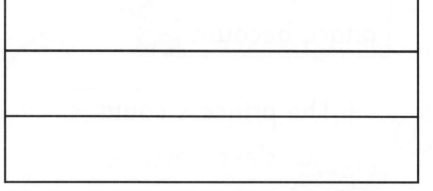

(2)

(3)

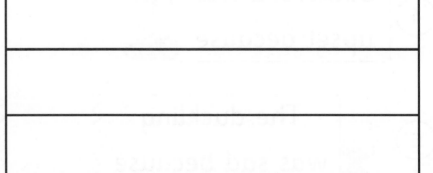

Today I scored ☐ out of 3.

Year 1 Phonics — Summer Term

Week 12 — Day 5

Draw a line to finish each sentence.

Daddy Bear is angry because

the witch locked him in a cage.

Goldilocks broke in.

(1) The princess could not sleep because

(2) The wolf was annoyed because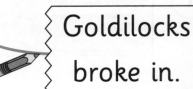

there was a pea in her bed.

(3) Hansel was scared because

she could not go to the Ball.

(4) Cinderella was upset because

they all said he was ugly.

(5) The duckling was sad because

he could not blow down the houses.

Today I scored ☐ out of 5.

Year 1 Phonics — Summer Term